Charles-Marie WIDOR

Suite

for Flute and Piano, Op. 34

Edited by

SIR JAMES GALWAY

Charles-Marie Widor, most famous for his organ music and as organist of *Saint Suplice* in Paris, was professor of composition and organ at the *Conservatoire National Superieur de Musique de Paris*. Widor's *Suite for Flute and Piano* was composed for Paul Taffanel (1844 - 1908), a fellow professor at the Conservatory who established the famous French School of flute playing. The work is in four movements and is one of my favorites to play in recital.

The first movement I tend to play on the slow side to bring out the strong "Schumanesque" feeling which haunts the first, third and fourth movements. By this, I mean it should be played with some *rubato* here and there to bring out the beauty of the musical line.

The second moment, *Allegro Vivace,* should be played very quickly to have the greatest impact. It was the favorite of Georges Barrère, who had it arranged for flute and orchestra. It is extremely difficult from a breathing standpoint and I would recommend following the breath marks I have inserted.

The third movement, *Andantino*, is one of rare beauty and should not be taken too slow. In this movement and the following *Vivace,* you have a great platform to show off your many different colors as a flutist.

The fourth movement is the real test piece of the suite. Marked "Vivace" you should not overdo the tempo, bearing in mind you are faced with the most virtuoso writing for the flute. Here again, I have inserted breath marks to help you play to the best of your ability. These are the breath marks I currently use in performing this beautiful and inspiring work. When deciding on the tempo of this movement, bear in mind the difficulties of the last page of this music.

The breath marks are of two kinds: (✓) being a very quick and short breath whereas (') is a regular breath mark. For a short breath, I would recommend that you don't open your mouth so much but that you acquire the technique of taking a lot of breath through your lips in the embouchure position.

Sir James Galway

to Paul Taffanel
Suite
for Flute and Piano

I.

Flute

Charles-Marie Widor, Op. 34
edited by Sir James Galway

Flute

Flute
II. Scherzo

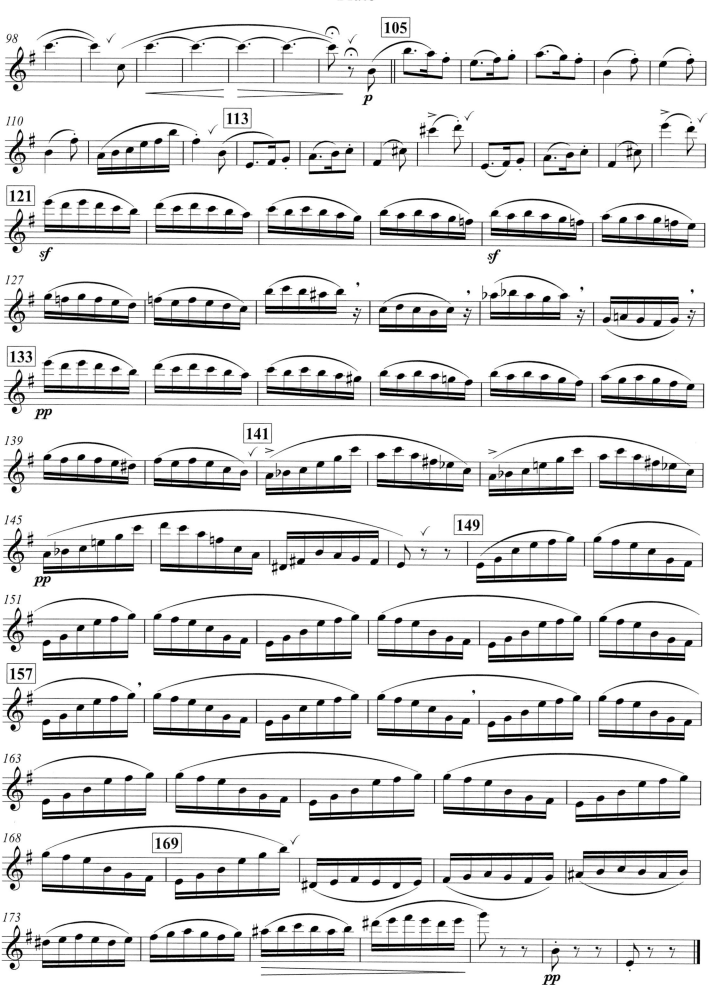

Flute

III. Romance

Flute

IV. Final

Flute

Digital and photographic copying of this page is illegal.

Flute

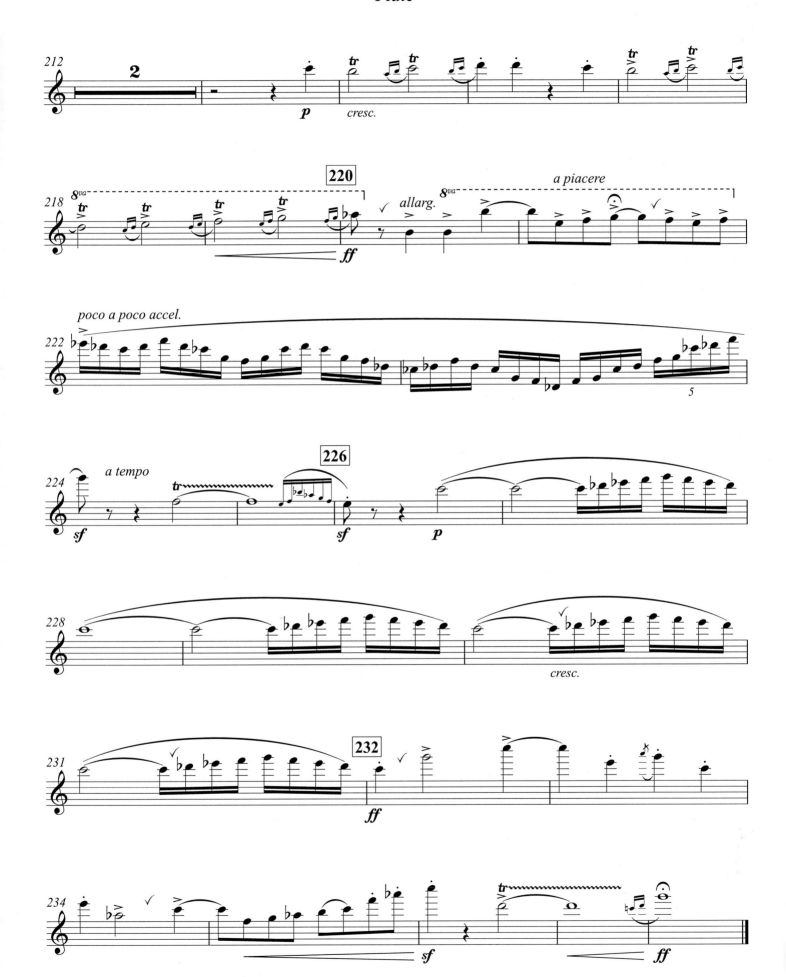